SCHOLASTIC

Do The Math

Created by
Marilyn Burns

Addition & Subtraction

Number Core

WorkSpace

Cover: © Guy Motil/Corbis

Copyright © 2011 by Scholastic Inc.

All rights reserved.   Published by Scholastic Inc.   Printed in the U.S.A.

ISBN-13: 978-0-545-33127-2
ISBN-10: 0-545-33127-7

SCHOLASTIC, DO THE MATH, and associated logos are trademarks and/or registe

7   8   9   10   40   20   19   18

 Pages printed on 10% PCW recycled pape

D1402904

Shake and Spill

1

Your partner shakes and spills 5 two-color counters.

2

Your partner puts the reds together and the yellows together and says how many of each.

3

Red	Yellow
3	2

You write the numbers of reds and yellows. Do steps 1–3 ten times. Then switch roles—you shake and spill and your partner writes the numbers of reds and yellows.

4

Equation
3 + 2 = 5

When you and your partner have the first two columns completed, write an equation for each spill.

	Red	Yellow	Equation
①	5	0	5+0=5
②	4	1	4+1=5
③	3	3	3+3=6
④	4	3	4+3=7
⑤	5	3	5+3=8
⑥	4	5	4+5=9
⑦	7	3	7+3=11
⑧	5	1	5+3
⑨	5	11	5+11=27
⑩			

Home Note: Your child writes equations with a sum of 5.

Game Rules for Race to the Top

What you need

- 5 two-color counters
- plastic cup
- *WorkSpace* pages 4 and 5
- pencil

➤ **One player shakes and spills while the other writes.**

1

3 Reds, 2 Yellows

Player A shakes and spills, groups the reds and yellows, and tells the number of each.

2

		3 + 2			
⑤ + ⓪	④ + ①	③ + ②	② + ③	① + ④	⓪ + ⑤

Player B writes the addition problem for reds plus yellows in the correct column.

3

Player A continues to shake and spill and Player B continues to write until Player B writes an addition problem in the top row.

4

Player A hands the cup and counters to Player B. Player A now writes while Player B shakes and spills.

Home Note: Your child writes addition problems for sums of 5.

Lesson 2

3

Race to the Top

HOW TO PLAY

1

Player A shakes and spills 5 two-color counters.

2

3 red   2 yellow

Player A puts the reds together and the yellows together and tells Player B the number of reds and yellows.

3

		3 + 2
⑤ + ⓪	④ + ①	③ + ②

Player B writes the addition problem in the first empty box above the matching problem. Player A does not write.

➤ **When Player B gets to the top row, switch roles.**

		3+2	2+3		0+5
		3+2	2+3		
⑤ + ⓪	④ + ①	③ + ②	② + ③	① + ④	⓪ + ⑤

4

Lesson 2

🏠 **Home Note:** Your child writes addition problems for sums of 5.

Race to the Top

HOW TO PLAY

1

Player A shakes and spills 5 two-color counters.

2

3 red   2 yellow

Player A puts the reds together and the yellows together and tells Player B the number of reds and yellows.

3

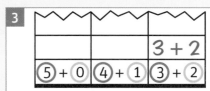

Player B writes the addition problem in the first empty box above the matching problem. Player A does not write.

➤ **When Player B gets to the top row, switch roles.**

⑤ + ⓪	④ + ①	③ + ②	② + ③	① + ④	⓪ + ⑤

Home Note: Your child writes addition problems for sums of 5.

Lesson 2   **5**

Write Equations for 6

DIRECTIONS

1

There are some reds on the ten-frame.

2

Draw yellows on the ten-frame so that there are 6 in all.

3

$2 + 4 = 6$

Write an equation for the colors.

4

$5 + 1 = 6$

Write an equation for the rows.

		Equation for Colors	**Equation for Rows**
①		$3R + 3Y =$	6
②		$4R + 2Y =$	6
③		$1R + 5Y =$	6
④		$5R + 1Y =$	6
⑤		$2R + 4Y$	6

Home Note: Your child writes equations for sums of 6.

Race to the Top for 6 Counters

1

Player A shakes and spills 6 two-color counters.

2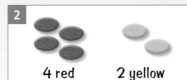

4 red   2 yellow

Player A puts the reds together and the yellows together and tells Player B the numbers of reds and yellows.

3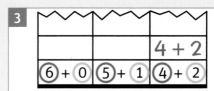

Player B writes the addition problem in the first empty box above the matching problem. Player A does not write.

➤ **When Player B gets to the top row, switch roles.**

⑥ + ⓪	⑤ + ①	④ + ②	③ + ③	② + ④	① + ⑤	⓪ + ⑥

Home Note: Your child writes addition problems for sums of 6.

Lesson 3

Roll and Add

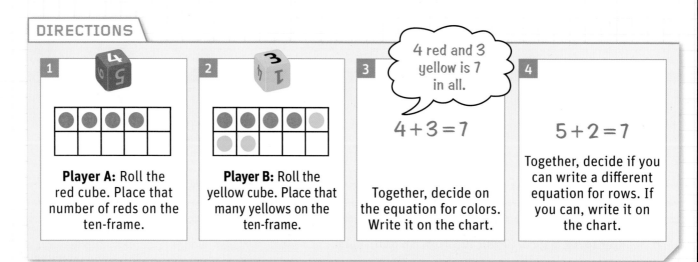

1 Player A: Roll the red cube. Place that number of reds on the ten-frame.

2 Player B: Roll the yellow cube. Place that many yellows on the ten-frame.

3 4 red and 3 yellow is 7 in all.

$4 + 3 = 7$

Together, decide on the equation for colors. Write it on the chart.

4 $5 + 2 = 7$

Together, decide if you can write a different equation for rows. If you can, write it on the chart.

	Equation for Colors	Equation for Rows
①		
②		
③		
④		
⑤		
⑥		
⑦		
⑧		
⑨		
⑩		

Lesson 4

Home Note: Your child writes equations with sums to 10.

Show What You Know

1

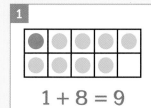

$1 + 8 = 9$

Write an equation
for colors.

2

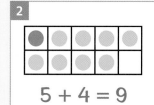

$5 + 4 = 9$

Write an equation
for rows.

		Equations			Equations
①		$3R + 5Y = 8$	②		$7R + 2Y = 9$
③		$2R + 5Y = 7$	④		$6R + 3Y = 9$
⑤		$4R + 5y = 9$	⑥		$2R + 4Y = 6$
⑦		$1R + 5Y = 6$	⑧		$8 + 1 = 9$
⑨		$3R + 6Y = 9$	⑩		$4 + 4 = 8$
⑪		$2r + 61 £$	⑫		$2 + 7 = 9$

Home Note: Your child writes equations with sums to 9.

Shake and Spill

1

Decide whether to shake and spill 7, 8, or 9 counters.

2

Your partner puts the reds together and the yellows together and says how many of each.

3

Red	Yellow
3	4

You write the numbers of reds and yellows. Do steps 1–3 ten times. Then switch roles—you shake and spill and your partner writes the numbers of reds and yellows.

4

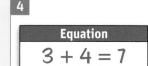

Equation
3 + 4 = 7

When you and your partner have the first two columns completed, write an equation for each spill.

	Red	Yellow	Equation
①			
②			
③			
④			
⑤			
⑥			
⑦			
⑧			
⑨			
⑩			

Home Note: Your child writes equations with a sum of 7, 8, or 9.

Sums of 10

DIRECTIONS

1

I have 6 reds. How many yellows to make 10?

Read the problem.

2

$6 +$ ___ $= 10$

Write an equation with a blank for the missing addend.

3

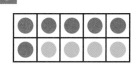

Place counters on the ten-frame to match the equation.

4

$6 +$ ___ $= 10$
$6 + 4 = 10$

Write an equation with the solution.

		Equations			Equations
①	I have 3 reds. How many yellows to make 10?	$3 + 7 = 10$	②	I have 9 reds. How many yellows to make 10?	$9 + 1 = 10$
③	I have 5 reds. How many yellows to make 10?	$5+5=10$	④	I have 10 reds. How many yellows to make 10?	$10+0=10$
⑤	I have 2 reds. How many yellows to make 10?	$2 + 8 = 10$	⑥	I have 1 red. How many yellows to make 10?	$1 + 9 = 10$
⑦	I have 7 reds. How many yellows to make 10?	$7 + 13 = 10$	⑧	I have 0 reds. How many yellows to make 10?	$0 + 10 = 10$
⑨	I have 4 reds. How many yellows to make 10?	$4+6 = 10$	⑩	I have 6 reds. How many yellows to make 10?	$6 + 4 = 10$
⑪	I have 8 reds. How many yellows to make 10?	$8+2=10$			

Home Note: Your child solves missing-addend problems for sums of 10.

Lesson 6

Add-to-10 Puzzles

DIRECTIONS

1

Draw a loop around the numbers
with a sum of 10.

2

Write the missing number to make
a sum of 10. Then loop the pair.

①

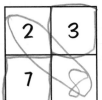

②

③

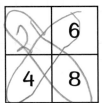

④

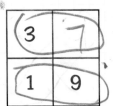

⑤

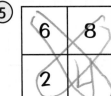

⑥

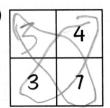

➤ **Loop pairs of numbers with a sum of 10. Pairs of numbers must touch either
on a side or at a corner.**

⑦

6	4	5	6
3	5	4	1
7	2	7	9
8	1	9	3

⑧

0	3	7	1
7	10	8	9
3	2	6	5
2	8	5	4

Home Note: Your child identifies number pairs with sums of 10.

Solve Addition Word Problems

DIRECTIONS

1	2	3	4
Deon has $4. He gets $3 as a gift. How much money does Deon have?	$4 + $3 = ___	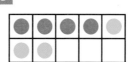	$4 + $3 = ___ $4 + $3 = $7
Read the problem.	Write an equation with a blank space.	Place counters on the ten-frame to match the equation.	Write an equation with the solution.

	Problems	Equations
①	Lamar has $2. He wants to buy a calculator for $10. How much more money does Lamar need?	$10^\cent - 2^\cent = 8^\#$
②	Mario rakes leaves after school. On Monday he earned $3. On Tuesday he earned $6. How much did Mario earn in all?	$^\$3 + ^\$6 = ^\$9$
③	Janelle and Henry are buying a gift. Janelle has $4. Henry has $5. Together how much money do they have for the gift?	$4 + 5^\$ = ^\$9$
④	Ana is saving money for a game. She has $2. The game costs $8. How much more money does Ana need to save?	$2^\cent - 8^\# = 6^\$$
⑤	Serena has $6 in her piggy bank. She has $4 in a penny jar. How much money does Serena have?	$6^\$ + 4^\$ = 10^\$$

Home Note: Your child writes equations and solves word problems.

Add-to-10 Puzzles

1

Draw a loop around the pair of numbers with a sum of 10.

2

Write the missing number to make a sum of 10. Then loop the pair.

①
2	6
8	4

②
1	7
	3

③
6	1
9	4

④
5	3
	5

⑤
6	8
2	4

⑥
3	5
6	7

> Loop pairs of numbers with a sum of 10. Pairs of numbers must touch either on a side or at a corner.

⑦
7	2	9	6
3	1	8	4
8	4	7	5
6	2	5	3

⑧
9	2	10	0
1	7	8	6
3	8	4	1
5	5	2	9

Home Note: Your child finds numbers with sums of 10.

How Many More to Make 10?

DIRECTIONS

1

How many counters do you see on the *Quick Look* card?

2

$4 + \_\_\_ = 10$

Write an equation with a blank for how many more to make 10.

3

$4 + \_\_\_ = 10$

$4 + 6 = 10$

Write an equation with the solution.

Number of Counters on *Quick Look* Card	Equations
①	$6 + 4 = 10$
②	$2 + 8 = 10$
③	$3 + 7 = 10$
④	$7 + 3 = 10$
⑤	$8 + 2 = 10$
⑥	$9 + 1 = 10$

Home Note: Your child writes equations and solves word problems.

Lesson 9

15

How Many More to Make 10?

DIRECTIONS

➤ Fill in the missing addend in each equation. You may use ten-frames and counters.

①	$8 + 2 = 10$	②	$5 + 5 = 10$	③	$1 + 9 = 10$
④	$3 + 7 = 10$	⑤	$10 + 0 = 10$	⑥	$7 + 3 = 10$
⑦	$6 + 4 = 10$	⑧	$0 + 10 = 10$	⑨	$4 + 6 = 10$

DIRECTIONS

1

Draw a loop around the pair of numbers with a sum of 10.

2

Write the missing number to make a sum of 10. Then loop the pair.

⑩

⑪
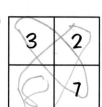

⑫

4	6
	9

⑬

4	2
8	

⑭

0	5
5	

⑮

4	
7	6

Home Note: Your child finds pairs of addends that make 10.

Show What You Know

➤ Draw a loop around the pair of numbers with a sum of 10.

➤ Write the missing number to make a sum of 10. Then loop the pair.

①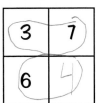

②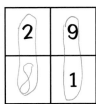

③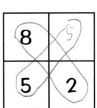

④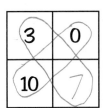

DIRECTIONS

➤ Read the problem.

➤ Write an equation with a blank. You may use your ten-frame and counters to help you.

➤ Write an equation with a solution.

Problem	Equations
⑤ Tanya had $4. She earned $6. How much money does Tanya have now?	6 + 4 = 10 $ 10
⑥ Owen blew up 3 balloons. He needs to blow up 10 in all. How many more balloons does Owen need to blow up?	3 + 7 = 10 10 a

DIRECTIONS

➤ Fill in the missing addend in each equation.

⑦ 8 + _2_ = 10	⑧ 6 + _4_ = 10
⑨ 3 + _7_ = 10	⑩ 1 + _9_ = 10

Home Note: Your child solves problems involving numbers with sums to 10.

Game Rules for Get to a 10

What you need
- *WorkSpace* page 19 or 20
- spinner (0–9)

➤ Players decide who will be Player X and who will be Player O. Players take turns.

➤ Each turn has 4 steps.

1

Spin the spinner.

2

3 + ____ = 10

Write an equation with a blank for the missing addend that makes 10.

3

3 + ____ = 10

3 + 7 = 10

Write an equation with the solution.

4

1 2 3 4 5 6 X̸ 8 9 10

Mark the missing addend with an X or O.

➤ If a player's missing addend already has an X or O on it, the player loses a turn.

➤ Play continues until all numbers are captured.

➤ The winner is the player with the most numbers captured. The game can end in a tie.

Home Note: Your child practices figuring how many more to make 10 by playing a game.

Get to a 10

➤ See the rules on page 18.

1   2   3   4   5   6   7   8   9   10

Equations	
Missing-addend Equation	Equation with Solution

1   2   3   4   5   6   7   8   9   10

Equations	
Missing-addend Equation	Equation with Solution

Home Note: Your child practices figuring how many more to make 10 by playing a game.

Lesson 10

19

Get to a 10

➤ See the rules on page 18.

1 2 3 4 5 6 7 8 9 10

Equations

Missing-addend Equation	Equation with Solution
9 + 🔲 = 10	9 + 1 = 10
8 + 🔲 = 10	8 + 2 = 10
5 + 🔲 = 10	5 + 5 = 10
6 + 🔲 = 10	6 + 3 = 10
2 + 🔲 = 10	2 + 8 = 10
4 + 🔲 = 10	4 + 6 = 10

1 2 3 4 5 6 7 8 9 10

Equations

Missing-addend Equation	Equation with Solution
5 + 🔲 = 10	5 + 5 = 10
5 + 🔲 = 10	5 + 5 = 10
9 + 🔲 = 10	9 + 1 = 10
6 + 🔲 = 10	6 + 3 = 10
5 + 🔲 = 10	5 + 5 = 10
4 + 🔲 = 10	4 + 6 = 10

Lesson 10

Home Note: Your child practices figuring how many more to make 10 by playing a game.

Relate Subtraction and Addition

1	2	3	4
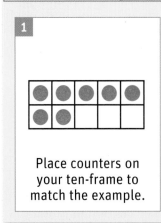 Place counters on your ten-frame to match the example.	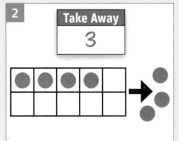 **Take Away** 3 — Take away counters and place to the side.	$7 - 3 = 4$ Write an equation.	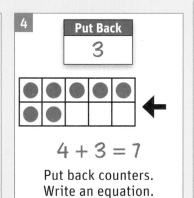 **Put Back** 3 — $4 + 3 = 7$ Put back counters. Write an equation.

		Take Away	Equation	Put Back	Equation
①	⚫⚫⚫⚫⚫ / ⚫⚫⚫	3	$8-3=5$	3	$8-3=5$
②	⚫⚫⚫⚫⚫ / ⚫⚫	5	$4-3=2$	5	$4-3=2$
③	⚫⚫⚫⚫⚫	4	$5-4=1$	4	$5-4=1$
④	⚫⚫⚫⚫ / ⚫⚫⚫	3	$4-3=6$	3	$4+3=6$
⑤	⚫⚫⚫⚫⚫ / ⚫⚫⚫⚫⚫	6	$10-6=4$	6	$10-6=4$
⑥	⚫⚫⚫⚫ / ⚫⚫⚫⚫	2	$8-2=6$	2	$8-2=6$
⑦	⚫⚫⚫⚫ / ⚫⚫	4	$4-4=3$	4	$7-4=3$
⑧	⚫⚫⚫⚫⚫ / ⚫⚫⚫⚫⚫	2	$10-2=8$	2	$10-2=8$

Home Note: Your child writes equations for subtraction and addition.

Lesson 11

Solve Addition and Subtraction Problems

Adriano

DIRECTIONS

1

There are 8 yo-yos in a box. Maya took out 3 yo-yos. How many yo-yos are left in the box?

Read the problem.

2

8 − 3 = ___

Write an equation with a blank space.

3

Model with counters on a ten-frame.

4

8 − 3 = 5

Write an equation with the solution.

Problems	Equations
① There are 7 yo-yos in the box. Ben took 4 yo-yos out of the box. How many yo-yos are left in the box?	7 − 4 = 3 yoyo's in the Box
② There are 8 yo-yos in the box. Tia took 7 yo-yos out of the box. How many yo-yos are left in the box?	8 − 7 = 1 yoyo's in the Box
③ There are 3 yo-yos in the box. Carl put 7 more yo-yos in the box. How many yo-yos are in the box?	3 + 7 = 10 yoyos in the Box
④ There are 4 yo-yos in the box. Li put 5 more yo-yos in the box. How many yo-yos are in the box?	4 + 5 = 9 yoyo's in the Box
⑤ There are 10 yo-yos in a box. Lin took 8 yo-yos out of the box. How many yo-yos are left in the box?	10 − 8 = 2 yoya's in the Box

22 Lesson 12

Home Note: Your child writes equations and solves word problems.

Game Rules for Empty the Box

What you need

- number cube (blue, 1–6)
- *WorkSpace* page 24 or 25
- ten-frame
- two-color counters

➤ **Players fill their ten-frames.**

➤ **Each turn has 3 steps. Players take turns.**

1

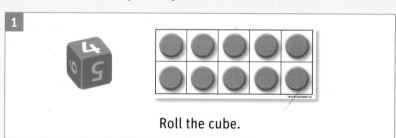

Roll the cube.

2

Roll	Equation
4	

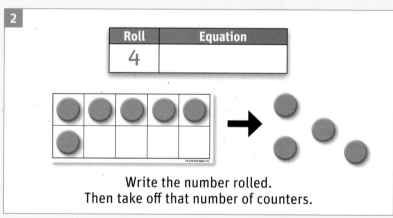

Write the number rolled.
Then take off that number of counters.

3

Roll	Equation
4	10 − 4 = 6

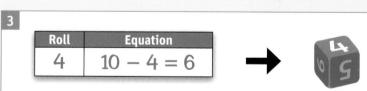

Write an equation and pass the number cube to your partner.

➤ **If you roll a number that is more than the number of counters on your ten-frame, you lose a turn.**

➤ **To clear the ten-frame, you must roll the exact number.**

➤ **The winner is the first player to empty the ten-frame.**

 Home Note: Your child practices subtraction by playing a game.

Lesson 13

23

Empty the Box

➤ See the rules on page 23.

Game 1	
Roll	**Equation**

Game 2	
Roll	**Equation**

Game 3	
Roll	**Equation**

Game 4	
Roll	**Equation**

Home Note: Your child practices subtraction by playing a game.

Empty the Box

> See the rules on page 23.

Game 5

Roll	Equation

Game 6

Roll	Equation

Game 7

Roll	Equation

Game 8

Roll	Equation

Home Note: Your child practices subtraction by playing a game.

Game Rules for Empty the Box 2

What you need
- number cube (blue, 1–6)
- *WorkSpace* page 27 or 28
- ten-frame
- two-color counters

➤ **Players fill their ten-frames.**

➤ **Each turn has 3 steps. Players take turns.**

1

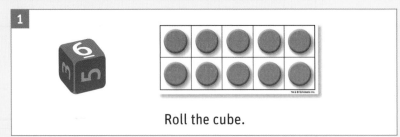

Roll the cube.

2

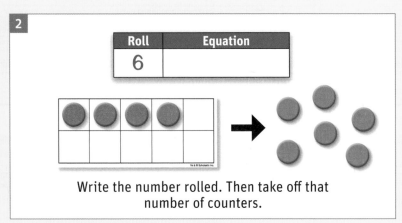

Roll	Equation
6	

Write the number rolled. Then take off that number of counters.

3

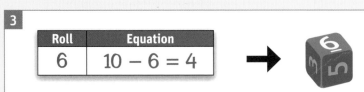

Roll	Equation
6	$10 - 6 = 4$

Write an equation and pass the number cube to your partner.

➤ **If you roll a number that is more than the number of counters on your ten-frame, add that number of counters to your ten-frame and write an equation with addition.**

➤ **The winner is the first player to empty the ten-frame.**

Home Note: Your child practices subtraction and addition by playing a game.

Empty the Box 2

> See the rules on page 26.

Game 1	
Roll	**Equation**

Game 2	
Roll	**Equation**

Game 3	
Roll	**Equation**

Game 4	
Roll	**Equation**

Home Note: Your child practices subtraction and addition by playing a game.

Empty the Box 2

➤ See the rules on page 26.

Game 5	
Roll	**Equation**

Game 6	
Roll	**Equation**

Game 7	
Roll	**Equation**

Game 8	
Roll	**Equation**

Home Note: Your child practices subtraction and addition by playing a game.

Show What You Know

DIRECTIONS

➤ Place counters on your ten-frame to match the example.
➤ Take away counters and place them to the side.
➤ Write an equation with subtraction.

	Ten-Frame	Take Away	Equation
①		4	6-4=2
②		2	9-2=7
③		5	8-5=3

DIRECTIONS

➤ Show the starting number by placing counters on your ten-frame.
➤ Decide whether you should add or subtract counters.
➤ Write an equation with a blank. Then write an equation with the solution.

	Problem	Equation
④	There are 6 yo-yos in the box. Sari put in 2 more yo-yos. How many yo-yos are in the box?	6+2=8 yoyos in the Box
⑤	There are 10 yo-yos in the box. Luis took out 6 yo-yos. How many yo-yos are left in the box?	10-6=4 yoyos in the Box

 Home Note: Your child solves problems and writes equations for subtraction and addition.

Empty the Box 2

> See the rules on page 26.

Game 1	
Roll	**Equation**

Game 2	
Roll	**Equation**

Game 3	
Roll	**Equation**

Game 4	
Roll	**Equation**

Home Note: Your child practices subtraction and writing equations by playing a game.

Game Rules for What's the Difference?

What you need

- *WorkSpace* page 32
- Ten-Frame Number Cards, one of each number 1–10
- two-color counters
- connecting cubes

> **Each turn has 4 steps. Play with a partner.**

1

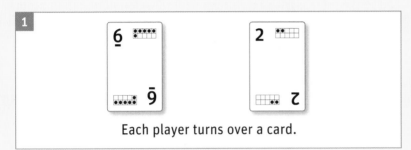

Each player turns over a card.

2

Each player builds a train for the numbers picked.

3

$$6 - 2 = 4$$

Compare the trains to find the difference.
Each player writes the equation.

4

The player who picked the card with the greater number captures the number of counters equal to the difference.

> **Play 5 rounds.**
> **Write the number of counters you captured.**
> **The winner is the player with more counters.**

Home Note: Your child practices subtraction and writing equations by playing a game.

What's the Difference?

➤ See the rules on page 31.

Game 1

Round	Equation
1	
2	
3	
4	
5	

How many counters did you capture? _____

Game 2

Round	Equation
1	
2	
3	
4	
5	

How many counters did you capture? _____

Game 3

Round	Equation
1	
2	
3	
4	
5	

How many counters did you capture? _____

Game 4

Round	Equation
1	
2	
3	
4	
5	

How many counters did you capture? _____

Home Note: Your child practices subtraction and writing equations by playing a game.

Solve Addition and Subtraction Problems

DIRECTIONS

1

Paul is 8 years old.
His sister is 5.
What is the difference?

Read the problem.

2

Make cube trains to help you solve the problem.

3

$8 - 5 = 3$

Write an equation.

Problems	Equations
① I had $10. I spent $9. How much do I have left?	10 - 9 = 1
② Jan has $9. Hal has $6. What is the difference?	9 + 6 = 15
③ Maya got $3 from her grandmother. Maya got $7 from her aunt. How much money does Maya have in all?	3 + 7 = 10
④ Mia has $2. She wants to buy a book for $10. How much more money does she need?	2 + 8 = 10
⑤ Norman has $6. Jay has $2. What is the difference?	6 + 2 = 8
⑥ Fran has 10 stamps. She uses 3 of them. How many does she have left?	10 - 3 - 7

Home Note: Your child writes equations and solves word problems.

What's the Difference?

➤ See the rules on page 31.

Game 1

Round	Equation
1	
2	
3	
4	
5	

How many counters did you capture? _____

Game 2

Round	Equation
1	
2	
3	
4	
5	

How many counters did you capture? _____

Game 3

Round	Equation
1	
2	
3	
4	
5	

How many counters did you capture? _____

Game 4

Round	Equation
1	
2	
3	
4	
5	

How many counters did you capture? _____

Home Note: Your child practices subtraction and writing equations by playing a game.

Two Ways to Subtract

1

$$7 - 3$$

Look at the problem.

2

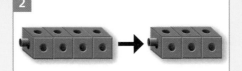

$$7 - 3 = 4$$

Use the take-away subtraction strategy. Write an equation.

3

$$3 + 4 = 7$$

Use the how-many-more addition strategy. Write an equation.

	Problem	Equation with Subtraction	Equation with Addition
①	10 – 8	$10 - 8 = 2$	$7 + 3 = 10$
②	8 – 6	$8 - 6 = 1$	$7 + 1 = 8$
③	7 – 1	$7 - 1 = 6$	$6 + 1 = 7$
④	8 – 3	$8 - 3 = 5$	$7 + 1 = 8$
⑤	9 – 2	$9 - 2 = 7$	$8 + 1 = 9$
⑥	6 – 2	$6 - 2 = 4$	$5 + 1 = 6$
⑦	10 – 4	$10 - 4 = 6$	$9 + 1 = 10$
⑧	9 – 3	$9 - 3 = 6$	$9 + 0 = 9$

Home Note: Your child solves subtraction problems with addition and subtraction.

Lesson 18

35

What's the Difference?

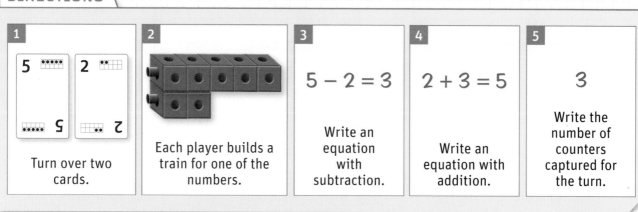

1	2	3	4	5
5 / 2 Turn over two cards.	Each player builds a train for one of the numbers.	5 − 2 = 3 Write an equation with subtraction.	2 + 3 = 5 Write an equation with addition.	3 Write the number of counters captured for the turn.

Game 1

Round	Equation with Subtraction	Equation with Addition	Number of Counters Captured
1			
2			
3			
4			
5			
		Total number of counters captured	

Game 2

Round	Equation with Subtraction	Equation with Addition	Number of Counters Captured
1			
2			
3			
4			
5			
		Total number of counters captured	

Home Note: Your child practices subtraction and writing equations by playing a game.

What's the Difference?

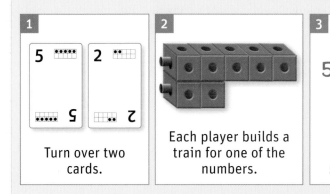

1
5 / 2

Turn over two cards.

2
Each player builds a train for one of the numbers.

3
$5 - 2 = 3$

Write an equation with subtraction.

4
$2 + 3 = 5$

Write an equation with addition.

5
3

Write the number of counters captured for the turn.

Game 1

Round	Equation with Subtraction	Equation with Addition	Number of Counters Captured
1			
2			
3			
4			
5			
		Total number of counters captured	

Game 2

Round	Equation with Subtraction	Equation with Addition	Number of Counters Captured
1			
2			
3			
4			
5			
		Total number of counters captured	

Home Note: Your child practices subtraction and writing equations by playing a game.

Lesson 18

37

What's the Difference?

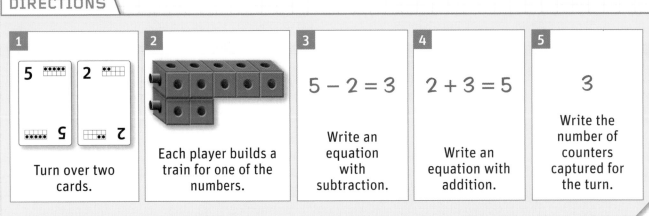

1 Turn over two cards.

2 Each player builds a train for one of the numbers.

3 $5 - 2 = 3$ Write an equation with subtraction.

4 $2 + 3 = 5$ Write an equation with addition.

5 3 Write the number of counters captured for the turn.

Game 1

Round	Equation with Subtraction	Equation with Addition	Number of Counters Captured
1			
2			
3			
4			
5			
		Total number of counters captured	

Game 2

Round	Equation with Subtraction	Equation with Addition	Number of Counters Captured
1			
2			
3			
4			
5			
		Total number of counters captured	

Home Note: Your child practices subtraction and writing equations by playing a game.

What's the Difference?

DIRECTIONS

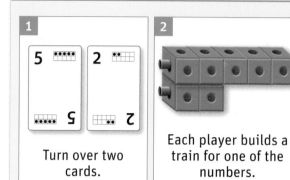

1

Turn over two cards.

2

Each player builds a train for one of the numbers.

3

$5 - 2 = 3$

Write an equation with subtraction.

4

$2 + 3 = 5$

Write an equation with addition.

5

3

Write the number of counters captured for the turn.

Game 1

Round	Equation with Subtraction	Equation with Addition	Number of Counters Captured
1			
2			
3			
4			
5			
		Total number of counters captured	

Game 2

Round	Equation with Subtraction	Equation with Addition	Number of Counters Captured
1			
2			
3			
4			
5			
		Total number of counters captured	

Home Note: Your child practices subtraction and writing equations by playing a game.

Game Rules for Hit the Target

What you need

- Ten-Frame Number Cards

➤ **Players take turns.**

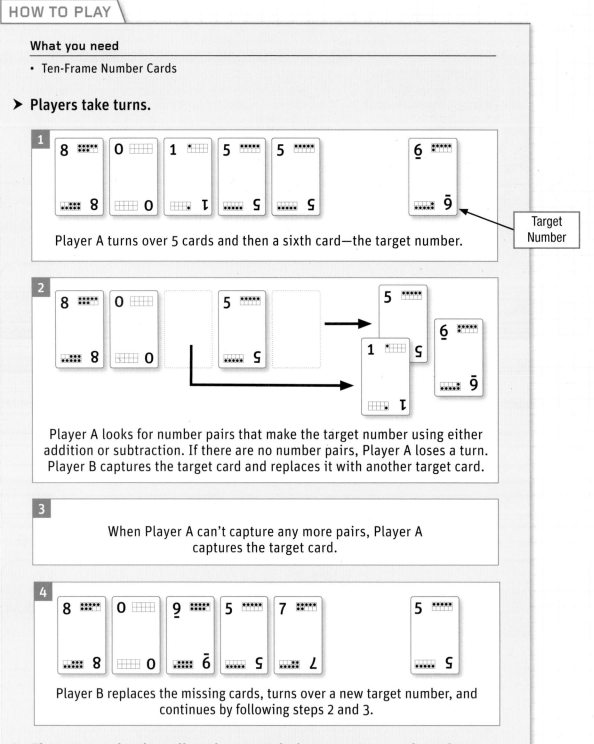

1 Player A turns over 5 cards and then a sixth card—the target number.

Target Number

2 Player A looks for number pairs that make the target number using either addition or subtraction. If there are no number pairs, Player A loses a turn. Player B captures the target card and replaces it with another target card.

3 When Player A can't capture any more pairs, Player A captures the target card.

4 Player B replaces the missing cards, turns over a new target number, and continues by following steps 2 and 3.

➤ **The game ends when all cards are used, there aren't enough cards to fill the spaces, or there are no more plays possible.**

➤ **The winner is the player who captures the most cards.**

Home Note: Your child practices subtraction by playing a game.

Show What You Know

DIRECTIONS

➤ Fill in the blanks in the equations.

4 + 2 = _6_	9 + 1 = _10_	2 + _8_ = 10
2 + 4 = _6_	1 + 9 = _10_	4 + _6_ = 10
5 + 5 = _10_	7 + 3 = _10_	3 + _7_ = 10
3 + 6 = _9_	3 + 7 = _10_	5 + _5_ = 10
10 − 1 = _9_	6 − 2 = _8_	9 − 8 = _1_
8 − 5 = _3_	10 − 7 = _3_	10 − 4 = _6_
9 − 4 = _5_	7 − 5 = _2_	7 − _2_ = 5
5 − 3 = _2_	8 − 3 = _5_	8 − _2_ = 6

DIRECTIONS

➤ Read the problem. Figure the answer. Then write an equation.

Problem	Equation
I blew up 4 balloons. I need to blow up 10 in all. How many more balloons do I need to blow up?	6
Bella scored 3 points in the game. Her sister scored 7 points. What is the difference in their scores?	4
Harry checked out 6 books at the library. He returned 2 of them. How many does he have left?	4

Home Note: Your child solves addition and subtraction problems.

Lesson 20   41

Writing Numbers to 20

DIRECTIONS

1

How many? __14__

Look at the ten-frames and write the number of counters.

2

___1___ ten and ___4___ ones

Fill in the blanks.

3

$14 = 10 + 4$

Write an equation.

How Many?	Fill in the Blanks	Equations
① How many? 16	__1__ ten and __4__ ones	14=10+4
② How many? 12	__1__ ten and __2__ ones	12=10+2
③ How many? 15	__1__ ten and __5__ ones	15=10+5
④ How many? ____	__1__ ten and __7__ ones	17=10+7
⑤ How many? ____	__1__ ten and __6__ ones	16=10+6
⑥ How many? ____	__1__ ten and __3__ ones	13=10+3
⑦ How many? ____	__1__ ten and __9__ ones	19=10+9
⑧ How many? ____	__2__ tens and __10__ ones	20=10+10

🏠 **Home Note:** Your child writes numbers to 20 as tens and ones.

Adding Numbers with Sums Greater than 10

DIRECTIONS

Move 2 to make 10. There are 5 left.

1

How many? __8__   How many? __7__

Look at the ten-frames and write the number of counters.

2

$8 + 7$

Write the addition problem. Think about how you would figure $8 + 7$ by making a 10.

3

$10 + 5 = 15$

$8 + 7 = 15$

Write equations.

How Many?		Addition Problem	Equations
① How many? _6_ How many? _9_		$6 + 9 = 15$	$5 + 10 = 15$ $6 + 9 = 15$
② How many? _1_ How many? __		$10 + 1 = 11$	$10 + 1 = 11$ $9 + 2 = 11$
③ How many? _9_ How many? _6_		$10 + 6 = 16$	$10 + 6 = 16$ $9 + 1 = 11$
④ How many? _8_ How many? _3_		$10 + 3 = 13$	$10 + 3 = 13$ $8 + 3 = 10$
⑤ How many? _6_ How many? __		$10 + 2 = 12$	$10 + 2 = 12$
⑥ How many? _1_ How many? __		$10 + 2 = 12$	$10 + 2 = 10$
⑦ How many? _8_ How many? __		$10 + 4 = 10$	$10 + 4 = 14$
⑧ How many? _5_ How many? __		$10 + 6 = 16$	$10 + 6 = 16$

Home Note: Your child adds Numbers with sums greater than 10.

43

Add Numbers with Sums Greater than 10

1	2	3	4
$6 + 8$ Look at the problem.	 Place counters on the ten-frames to match the problem.	$6 + 8 = 14$ Write an equation for colors.	$10 + 4 = 14$ Write an equation for ten-frames.

Problem	Equation for Colors	Equation for Ten-frames
$8 + 9$		$8 + 9 = 16$
$7 + 7$		$7 + 7 = 14$
$6 + 6$		$6 + 6 = 11$
$5 + 8$		$5 + 8 = 13$

Home Note: Your child adds numbers with sums greater than 10.

Game Rules for Oh No! Not a 10

HOW TO PLAY

What you need

- *WorkSpace* page 46
- Ten-Frame Number Cards
- ten-frames
- two-color counters

➤ **Players take turns. Each turn has 3 steps.**

1

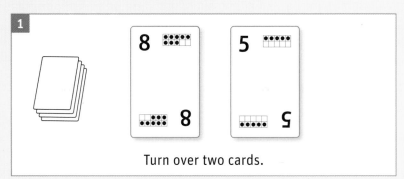

Turn over two cards.

2

Add the numbers. It's OK to use ten-frames and counters.

3

More than 10	Less than 10
$8 + 5 = 13$	

Write the equation in the correct column. If the column is full, you don't write the equation and your turn is over.

➤ **A player loses a turn if the sum of the two cards is 10.**

➤ **The winner is the first to fill his or her chart with 10 equations.**

➤ **If all of the cards have been turned over and no player has 10 equations, mix the cards, place the cards in a stack facedown, and continue turning over two cards.**

Home Note: Your child practices adding one-digit numbers by playing a game.

Oh No! Not a 10

> ➤ See the rules on page 45.

Game 1

More Than 10	Less Than 10

Game 2

More Than 10	Less Than 10

Game 3

More Than 10	Less Than 10

Game 4

More Than 10	Less Than 10

Game 5

More Than 10	Less Than 10

Game 6

More Than 10	Less Than 10

Home Note: Your child practices subtraction and writing equations by playing a game.

Use Addition Strategies

DIRECTIONS

➤ Use the put-the-greater-addend-first strategy.

➤ Write the sums.

① 3 + 9 = 12	② 2 + 9 = 11	③ 1 + 14 = 15
④ 2 + 16 = 18	⑤ 1 + 10 = 11	⑥ 2 + 12 = 14

DIRECTIONS

➤ Use the doubles-plus-1 strategy or the doubles-minus-1 strategy.

➤ Write the sums.

⑦ 4 + 5 = 9	⑧ 9 + 10 = 19	⑨ 7 + 6 = 13
⑩ 8 + 7 = 14	⑪ 5 + 6 = 11	⑫ 8 + 9 = 17

DIRECTIONS

➤ Choose a strategy.

➤ Write the sums.

⑬ 1 + 5 = 6	⑭ 1 + 17 = 18	⑮ 8 + 7 = 15
⑯ 6 + 5 = 11	⑰ 2 + 10 = 12	⑱ 1 + 13 = 14
⑲ 2 + 14 = 16	⑳ 3 + 11 = 14	㉑ 9 + 8 = 17
㉒ 10 + 9 = 19	㉓ 3 + 16 = 19	㉔ 6 + 7 = 13

Home Note: Your child uses strategies to add numbers mentally.

Lesson 24

47

Game Rules for Addition Five-in-a-Row

What you need

• *WorkSpace* page 49 or 51
• spinner (0–9)

1

9

Player A spins and both players write the
number on their own chart.

2

9   5

Player B spins and both players write the
number on their own chart.

3

9   5

9 + 5 = 14

Both players add the numbers and agree on the sum.
Then they each write an equation on their own chart.

4

13	Doubles	14 9 + 5 = 14
17	18	Free Choice

> This shows a partial game board.

Each player writes the equation in one box on their game
board, either in the box with that sum, in a Free Choice box,
or in a box with Doubles if both addends are the same.

➤ **If there are no open boxes to write an equation, each player
spins again to get a new equation.**

➤ **The winner is the first player to write equations in 5 boxes
in a row.**

Home Note: Your child practices adding numbers with sums to 18 by playing a game.

Addition Five-in-a-Row

DIRECTIONS

➤ Write equations in the chart at the top of the page and then in one of the boxes of the game board.

First Number	Second Number	Equation

Free Choice	0	1	2	3
4	Doubles	5	Doubles	6
7	8	9	10	11
12	Doubles	13	Doubles	14
15	16	17	18	Free Choice

Home Note: Your child practices addition with sums to 18 by playing a game.

Show What You Know

DIRECTIONS

➤ Write the sums.

4 + 5 = _9_	9 + 8 = _17_	2 + 9 = _11_	1 + 15 = _16_
6 + 7 = _12_	3 + 8 = _11_	4 + 8 = _12_	2 + 17 = _19_
5 + 6 = _11_	7 + 8 = _15_	6 + 8 = _14_	8 + 8 = _17_
9 + 9 = _18_	9 + 6 = _15_	7 + 7 = _14_	5 + 10 = _15_

DIRECTIONS

➤ Write the number of tens and ones.

17 = _10_ ten(s) + _10_ one(s)
20 = _0_ ten(s) + _10_ one(s)
13 = _10_ ten(s) + _0_ one(s)
18 = _10_ ten(s) + _10_ one(s)

Home Note: Your child adds numbers with sums to 20.

Addition Five-in-a-Row

➤ Write equations in the chart at the top of the page and then in one of the boxes of the game board.

First Number	Second Number	Equation

Free Choice	0	1	2	3
4	Doubles	5	Doubles	6
7	8	9	10	11
12	Doubles	13	Doubles	14
15	16	17	18	Free Choice

Home Note: Your child practices addition with sums to 18 by playing a game.

Add Clocks

➤ Use the groups of clocks to answer the questions.

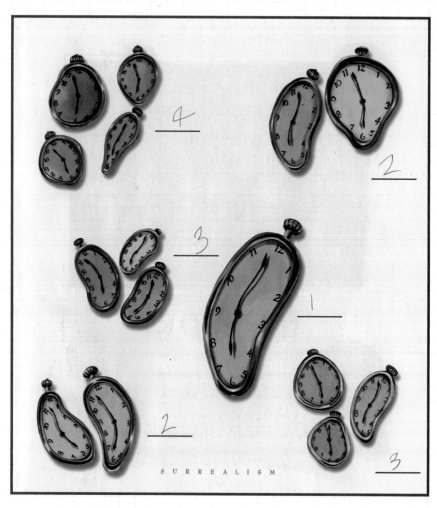

SURREALISM

1. Write the number of clocks in each group on the blank lines in the picture.

2. Write an equation to show the:

   a. sum of clocks in the first row.
   4+2=6

   b. sum of clocks in the second row.
   3+1=4

   c. sum of clocks in the third row.
   2+3=5

   d. total number of clocks (use the sums of the rows).
   4+2+3+1+2+3=

3. Write an equation to show the:

   a. sum of clocks on the left side. _____

   b. sum of clocks on the right side. _____

   c. total number of clocks (use the sums of the sides). _____

Home Note: Your child solves addition problems with two or more addends.

Use Addition Strategies

DIRECTIONS

➤ Find the sums by making a 10.

①	5 + 6 + 5 = __16__	②	1 + 7 + 9 = __17__
③	3 + 2 + 8 = __13__	④	4 + 3 + 6 = __13__

DIRECTIONS

➤ Add the numbers across and write the sums in the circles.

➤ Add the numbers going down and write the sums in the circles.

➤ Use the make-a-10 strategy or the doubles strategy to figure the sums.

⑤

4	8	6	◯ 7
8	2	7	◯
6	6	4	◯

◯ ◯ ◯

⑥

9	1	5	◯
9	3	7	◯
1	9	5	◯

◯ ◯ ◯

⑦

6	6	4	◯
7	7	3	◯
4	3	6	◯

◯ ◯ ◯

Home Note: Your child solves addition problems with two or more addends.

Addition Five-in-a-Row

DIRECTIONS

➤ Write equations in the chart at the top of the page and then in one of the boxes of the game board.

First Number	Second Number	Equation

Free Choice	0	1	2	3
4	Doubles	5	Doubles	6
7	8	9	10	11
12	Doubles	13	Doubles	14
15	16	17	18	Free Choice

Home Note: Your child practices addition with sums to 18 by playing a game.

Game Rules for Subtraction Five-in-a-Row

What you need
- *WorkSpace* page 56 or 57
- Ten-Frame Number Cards, four of each number 6–9

1

First Number	Second Number	Equation
13		

Player A chooses a number from 11 to 15.
Both players write the number on their own chart.

2

First Number	Second Number	Equation
13	7	

Player B turns over a card. Both players
write that number on their own chart.

3

First Number	Second Number	Equation
13	7	13 − 7 = 6

Both players subtract the numbers and agree on the difference.
Then they each write an equation on their own chart.

4

> This shows a partial game board.

6	8	Free Choice
13 − 7 = 6		

Each player writes the equation in one box on their game board,
either in a box with that difference or in a Free Choice box.

➤ It's possible that only one player is able to make a play on a turn. If neither player has an open box to write an equation, begin a new turn.

➤ The winner is the first player to write equations in 5 boxes in a row.

Home Note: Your child solves subtraction problems with addition.

Subtraction Five-in-a-Row

➤ Write equations in the chart at the top of the page and then in one of the boxes of the game board.

First Number	Second Number	Equation

Free Choice	5	6	8	Free Choice
4	7	6	9	5
5	7	Free Choice	3	6
4	4	5	2	8
Free Choice	6	3	7	Free Choice

Home Note: Your child practices figuring differences by playing a game.

Subtraction Five-in-a-Row

> ➤ Write equations in the chart at the top of the page
> and then in one of the boxes of the game board.

First Number	Second Number	Equation

Free Choice	5	6	8	Free Choice
4	7	6	9	5
5	7	Free Choice	3	6
4	4	5	2	8
Free Choice	6	3	7	Free Choice

Home Note: Your child practices figuring differences by playing a game.

Add Spots

DIRECTIONS

➤ Use the groups of spots to answer the questions.

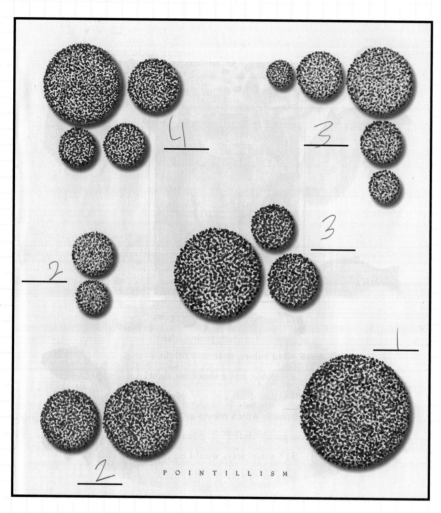

4

3

2

3

3

2

POINTILLISM

1 Write the number of spots in each group on the blank lines in the picture.

2 Write an equation to show the:

a. sum of spots in the first row.
   4 ∨ 3

b. sum of spots in the second row.
   2 + 3 = 5

c. sum of spots in the third row.
   2 + 1 = 3

d. total number of spots (use the sums of the rows).
   4 + 3 + 2 + 3 + 2 + 1 = 15

3 Write an equation to show the:

a. sum of spots on the left side. 4 + 2 + 2 = 8

b. sum of spots on the right side. 3 + 3 + 1 = 7

c. total number of spots (use the sums of the left and right sides). _____

Home Note: Your child solves addition problems with two or more addends.

Add Umbrellas

DIRECTIONS

➤ Use the groups of umbrellas to answer the questions.

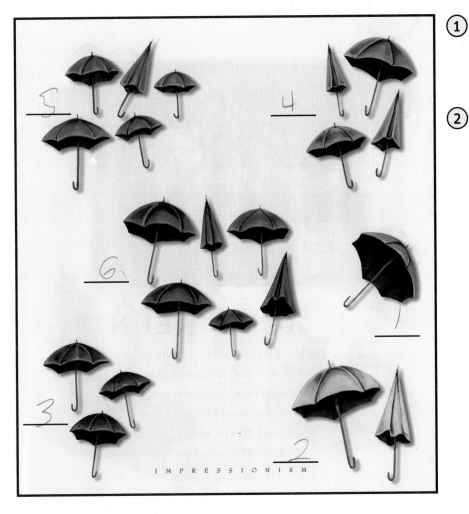

IMPRESSIONISM

(1) Write the number of umbrellas in each group on the blank lines in the picture.

(2) Write an equation to show the:

a. sum of umbrellas in the first row.

$5+4=9$

b. sum of umbrellas in the second row.

$6+1=7$

c. sum of umbrellas in the third row.

$3+2=5$

d. total number of umbrellas (use the sums of the rows).

$5+4+6+1+2+3=21$

(3) Write an equation to show the:

a. sum of umbrellas on the left side. $4+1+2=7$

b. sum of umbrellas on the right side. $3+6+3=14$

c. total number of umbrellas (use the sums of the left and right sides). $5+6+3+2+4=21$

Home Note: Your child solves addition problems with two or more addends.

Show What You Know

DIRECTIONS

➤ Figure the sums.

①	$2 + 3 + 1 + 2 + 4 =$ _12_	②	$5 + 2 + 3 + 3 + 1 =$ _19_
③	$2 + 4 + 4 + 8 =$ _18_	④	$7 + 6 + 3 =$ _16_

DIRECTIONS

➤ Add the numbers across and write the sums in the circles.
➤ Add the numbers going down and write the sums in the circles.

⑤

4	7	6	6
5	3	5	4
6	9	4	0

(4) (3) (0)

⑥

1	2	9	8
7	8	2	2
9	3	1	6

(7) (2) (1)

DIRECTIONS

➤ Figure the differences.

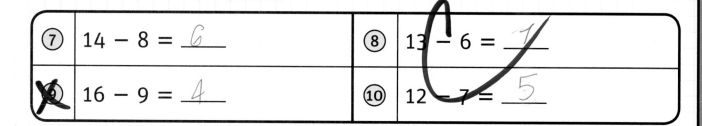

⑦	$14 - 8 =$ _6_	⑧	$13 - 6 =$ _7_
⑨	$16 - 9 =$ _4_	⑩	$12 - 7 =$ _5_

Lesson 30   **Home Note:** Your child solves addition and subtraction problems.

Game Rules for Addition Capture

HOW TO PLAY

What you need
- *WorkSpace* pages 62 and 63
- *Addition Capture* cards (13 cards for each player)

➤ **Each turn has 3 steps.**

1

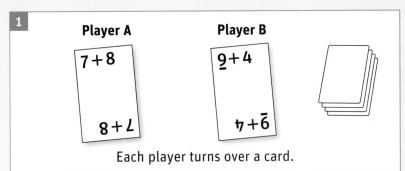

Each player turns over a card.

2

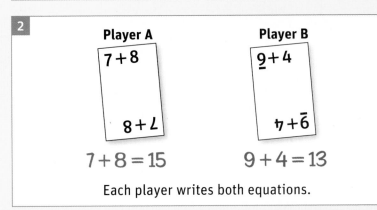

Each player writes both equations.

3

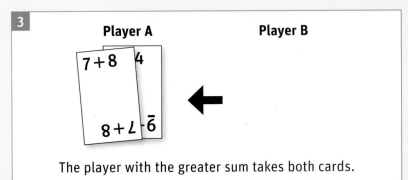

The player with the greater sum takes both cards.

➤ **If the sums are the same for both players' cards, they each turn over another card. The player with the greater sum gets all 4 cards.**

➤ **When all the cards have been used, the winner is the player who has captured more cards.**

 Home Note: Your child practices addition by playing a game.

Addition Capture

DIRECTIONS

➤ See the game rules on page 61.

➤ Write both your equations and your partner's equations.

Player A	Player B

Lesson 30

Home Note: Your child practices addition by playing a game.

Addition Capture

DIRECTIONS

➤ See the game rules on page 61.

➤ Write both your equations and your partner's equations.

Player A	Player B

Home Note: Your child practices addition by playing a game.

Math Vocabulary

➤ Write new words and terms in the box.

➤ Write a definition, show an example, or draw a picture for each word or term in your list.

Math Vocabulary

Home Note: Your child creates a math vocabulary list.

Math Vocabulary

➤ Write new words and terms in the box.

➤ Write a definition, show an example, or draw a picture for each word or term in your list.

Home Note: Your child creates a math vocabulary list.

Glossary

add

Add is what you do to find the sum or total number when two or more numbers are joined or put together. For example, we can add or join 4 and 2. We write 4 + 2. The plus symbol (+) tells you to add.

4 + 2 asks the question *How many in all?* If there are 4 reds and 2 yellows on a ten-frame, we can say there are 6 counters in all.

This ten-frame shows 4 + 2 = 6.
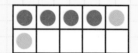

addend

The numbers being added are called *addends*. In the equation 4 + 2 = 6, 4 and 2 are addends. There may be more than two addends. For 2 + 3 + 2 + 1 = 8, there are four addends—2, 3, 2, and 1.

addition

Addition is the name for what you do when you add. When you add two numbers together you are doing *addition*.

comparing problem

A *comparing problem* asks you to figure the difference between two numbers. It can be solved with addition or subtraction. In a comparing problem you don't take anything away.

Here is an example of a comparing problem:
Fred is 10 years old.
His brother Ted is 6 years old.
What is the difference in their ages?

You can solve this problem with subtraction. 10 − 6 = _____. Or you can solve it with addition. 6 + _____ = 10. Either way, you get the same answer of 4. Fred is 4 years older than Ted.

difference

When you are figuring the difference between two numbers, you figure how much more or less one number is than the other. Also, when you solve any subtraction problem, the answer is called the *difference*.

digit

In a number, the numerals 0 to 9 are called *digits*. In 28, the digits are 2 and 8. 28 is a two-digit number because there is a digit in each of the two places—ones and tens.

equal

Equal means the same amount. The symbol for equal is =. It means that whatever is on one side of the symbol has the same value as what is on the other side of the symbol.

For example, in 4 + 2 = 3 + 3 both the left side and the right side of the = symbol have the same value—6.

equation

An *equation* is a mathematical sentence that uses an equals symbol (=) to show that two amounts have the same value.

For example, 3 + 4 = 7 is an equation because 3 + 4 and 7 have the same value, and that is shown with the equals symbol between them.

Glossary

joining problem

A *joining problem* is a problem that is solved with addition. It is called joining because you add or join two things together.

Here is an example of a joining problem:

> I had $4.
> I got $5 more.
> How much money do I have now?

You can solve by joining or adding $4 and $5 to get $9. $4 + $5 = $9.

minus

The word *minus* shows that you are doing subtraction. 7 minus 3 is a subtraction problem. You subtract or take away 3 from 7 to find out how much is left, 4. The symbol for minus is $-$. You can write 7 minus 3 as $7 - 3$.

To subtract 3 from 7, you can also find the difference by adding. $3 + \underline{} = 7$. The answer is 4 either way.

missing-addend problem

In a *missing-addend problem*, you know the sum or total and one addend, and you need to figure out the other addend.

$3 + \underline{} = 9$ is an example of a missing-addend problem. The missing addend is 6 because $3 + 6 = 9$.

one-digit number

A *one-digit number* is any number from 0 to 9.

place value

When a number has more than one digit, the position or place of a digit tells its value. For example, in the number 11, the first 1 has a different value than the second 1. The value of the first 1 is 10 and the value of the second 1 is 1. Where the 1 is placed determines its value. This is why we say our number system is a place-value system—where a digit is placed determines its value.

plus

The word *plus* tells you to add. 3 plus 3 means you should add 3 and 3. The symbol for plus is $+$.

subtract

Subtract is what you do when you take away one number from another, or when you find the difference between two numbers. For example, to solve a problem such as:

> I had $9.
> I spent $4.
> How much do I have left?

You can take away 4 from 9, or you can figure the difference between 4 and 9. The answer is $5. The answer to a subtraction problem is called the *difference*.

Glossary

subtraction

Subtraction is what you do to find out how much is left when you take away an amount. For example, *I had $7. I spent $3. How much do I have now?* When you figure the answer, you are doing subtraction.

Subtraction is also what you do when you have two amounts and you compare them to see how much more one is than the other. For example, *I have $7. Ty has $3. How much more do I have?* When you figure the answer, you are doing subtraction.

You can also use subtraction to solve a missing-addend problem. For example, *My book has 7 pages. I read 4 pages. How many more do I need to read to finish the book?* The equation for this problem is 4 + ____ = 7. To figure the answer, you could do subtraction and think, "7 minus 4 equals what number?" Or you could do addition and think, "4 plus what number equals 7?"

sum

The *sum* is the answer you get when you add two or more numbers. In the equation 4 + 1 = 5, 5 is the sum.

We can ask the question, "What is the sum of 2 and 3?" This is the same as asking, "What is 2 plus 3?"

symbols

You use *symbols* in mathematics to name numbers (12, 308, $\frac{1}{2}$), operations ($+, -, \times, \div$), and relationships between numbers ($=, >, <$).

take-away problem

A *take-away problem* is one kind of subtraction problem. There is a starting amount and an amount taken away. For example:

> Abe has $10.
> He spent $6.
> How much money does Abe have left?

10 – 6 = 4 so Abe has $4 left.

two-digit number

Two-digit numbers are numbers from 10 to 99. In every two-digit number, the first digit tells you the number of tens and the second digit tells how many ones. 12 is a two-digit number—1 ten and 2 ones or 10 + 2.

My Notes

My Notes

My Notes

My Notes